big
NATE
OUT LOUD

More

big NATE

adventures from

LINCOLN PEIRCE

---

big NATE

OUT LOUD

by LINCOLN PEIRCE

Andrews McMeel
PUBLISHING®

Big Nate is distributed internationally by Andrews Mcmeel Syndication.

Big Nate Out Loud copyright © 2011 by United Feature Syndicate, Inc. All rights reserved. Printed in China. No part of this book may be used or reproduced in any manner whatsoever without written permission except in the case of reprints in the context of reviews.

Andrews Mcmeel Publishing
a division of Andrews Mcmeel Universal
1130 Walnut Street, Kansas City, Missouri 64106

www.andrewsmcmeel.com

17 18 19 20 21 SDB 20 19 18 17 16

ISBN: 978-1-4494-0718-6

Library of Congress Control Number: 2011920757

These strips appeared in newspapers from
April 2, 2007, through November 4, 2007.

Made by:
Shenzhen Donnelley Printing Company Ltd.
Address and place of production:
No. 47, Wuhe Nan Road, Bantian Ind. Zone,
Shenzhen China, 518129
16th Printing—8/14/17

Big Nate can be viewed on the Internet at
www.gocomics.com/big_nate

ATTENTION: SCHOOLS AND BUSINESSES
Andrews Mcmeel books are available at quantity discounts with bulk purchase for educational, business, or sales promotional use. For information, please e-mail the Andrews Mcmeel Publishing Special Sales Department:
specialsales@amuniversal.com.

For the Rhode Islanders

I'M GOING TO CHALLENGE MARCUS AS THE SCHOOL'S NUMBER ONE TRENDSETTER!

YOU'RE CRAZY. MARCUS IS THE MAN.

HE WAS THE FIRST KID TO POST ON YOUTUBE, THE FIRST TO START WEARING BOWLING SHOES, THE FIRST TO...

EX**ACT**LY! WHY SHOULD **HE** GET TO DETERMINE WHAT'S COOL?

WHY SHOULDN'T **I** GET TO DETERMINE WHAT'S COOL?

...ASKED THE KID WITH THE "AGENT CODY BANKS" WRIST-WATCH.

HEY, THAT'S **RETRO**! THAT'S A **COLLECT-IBLE**!

I LOVE THIS TIME OF YEAR! IT'S JOB-FREE!

JOB-FREE?

NO RESPONSIBILITIES, TEDDY!

THE SNOW HAS MELTED, SO THERE'S NOTHING TO SHOVEL...

THE GRASS HASN'T STARTED GROWING YET, SO THERE'S NOTHING TO **MOW**...

...AND THERE AREN'T ANY **LEAVES** ON THE GROUND, SO THERE'S NOTHING TO **RAKE**!

NO RESPONSIBILITIES! JOB-FREE!

WRIGHT

WHAT A REVOLTING TURN OF EVENTS.

DANG IT!

NATE, I'VE HEARD ENOUGH NONSENSE ABOUT YOUR LOCKER BEING SOME SORT OF PERSONAL **TREASURE TROVE**!

IT'S **TRASH**, PURE AND SIMPLE! AND I WANT IT CLEANED UP IN THE NEXT **TEN MINUTES**!!

NOT **TWELVE** MINUTES! NOT **ELEVEN** MINUTES! I EXPECT YOU... YOU...

NATE?

A MESSY LOCKER DOES HAVE ITS ADVANTAGES.

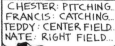

CHESTER: PITCHING...
FRANCIS: CATCHING...
TEDDY: CENTER FIELD...
NATE: RIGHT FIELD...

AGAIN?

WELL, WHY NOT? YOU'RE A VERY GOOD RIGHT FIELDER!

YEAH, BUT...

NOTHING EVER **HAPPENS** OUT THERE!

THAT'S JUST THE WAY BASEBALL IS, NATE. SOMETIMES THEY HIT IT TO YOU, AND SOMETIMES THEY DON'T!

YEAH, I KNOW...

...BUT IT'S JUST SO **BORING** STANDING AROUND FOR NINE INNINGS!

JUST GET OUT THERE, NATE. I'M SURE YOU'LL FIND **SOME** WAY TO KEEP YOURSELF AMUSED.

SIGH...

HEY, MAYBE WE CAN **HYPNO-TIZE** YOU INTO BE-COMING NEATER!

IT WORKED **BEFORE**, REMEMBER? FRANCIS AND I HYPNOTIZED YOU TO FIND OUT WHY YOU'RE AFRAID OF CATS!

YOU'RE AFRAID OF CATS?

NATE'S AFRAID OF CATS!

THANKS **SO** MUCH.

OOPS.

HERE'S MY HOMEWORK, MRS. GODFREY! YOU WANT **NEAT**? YOU'VE **GOT** NEAT!

NO RIPS, NO WRINKLES, NO SMUDGES, NO STAINS! ABSOLUTELY NO MISTAKES OF ANY KIND!

YOU WERE SUPPOSED TO ANSWER THE TEN QUESTIONS AT THE END OF CHAPTER TWO, NOT THE TWO QUESTIONS AT THE END OF CHAPTER TEN.

OKAY, ONE TEENSY LITTLE MISTAKE.

TRY AGAIN.

I MEAN, THE GRASS IS SORT OF PATCHY... THERE'S A PUDDLE OVER THERE... AND ALL THESE ACORNS SEEM SORT OF... YOU KNOW... RANDOM.

..MMPH!... I FELL ASLEEP! WHAT'S HAPPENING?

THEY'RE GOING OVER THE SCHOOL BUDGET, LINE BY LINE.

RIGHT NOW THEY'RE DISCUSSING THE "GIFTED AND TALENTED" PROGRAM, OF WHICH I WAS A PART BACK IN THE DAY!

YOU WERE "GIFTED AND TALENTED"?

I WAS INDEED, MON AMI!

WAIT, WAIT. YOU WERE...?

I SAID YES, KID. GO BACK TO SLEEP.

Peirce

OKAY, MR. GALVIN...
HERE'S A JOKE
I THINK YOU'LL
APPREC-
IATE!

WHAT DID THE
THEORETICAL PHYSICIST
USE TO DRINK
HIS BEER?

AN
EIN-
STEIN!

WA HA HA
HA HA
HO HO
HA

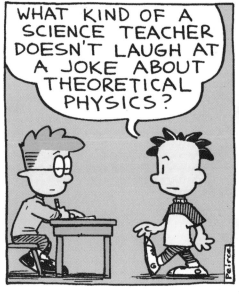

WHAT KIND OF A
SCIENCE TEACHER
DOESN'T LAUGH AT
A JOKE ABOUT
THEORETICAL
PHYSICS?

GUYS, I CONVINCED CHAD TO JOIN THE CARTOONING CLUB!

COOL!

HEY, CHAD.

PULL UP A CHAIR, CHAD!

UH...WHERE ARE ALL THE GIRLS?

YOU SAID THERE WERE LOTS OF GIRLS AT THESE MEETINGS.

RIGHT! GIRLS WE **DRAW!**

MY NEWEST CHARACTER: RAMONA BOMBSHELLE!

ROWR! HEL-**LO!**

WHEN DRAWING COMICS, CHAD, COMING UP WITH THE RIGHT SOUND EFFECT IS **CRUCIAL!**

ALMOST ANY SITUATION CAN BE MADE FUNNY BY THE ADDITION OF A HUMOROUS SOUND EFFECT!

KLONG!

PROPS ARE ALSO KEY!

OW!

YOU'RE **BOTH** RIGHT!

WHEN DRAWING A COMIC STRIP, CHAD, YOU DON'T ALWAYS HAVE TO WAIT UNTIL THE FINAL PANEL TO DELIVER THE PUNCH LINE!

SOMETIMES YOU CAN PUT THE JOKE IN THE **NEXT-TO-LAST** PANEL! THEN THE **LAST** PANEL CAN BE JUST, YOU KNOW, A REACTION SHOT!

WOO WOO WOO WOO WOO

BOING! BOING!

NOW, WHERE WAS I?

Peirce

WHATCHA READING THERE, MRS. CZERWICKI?

ER... WELL...

"PYRAMIDS OF PASSION"! OOOH! LET'S TAKE A LOOK AT THE BACK COVER, SHALL WE?

ZIP!

"WHILE EXCAVATING THE TOMB OF HAKHOTAN, SHAPELY SCIENTIST MAURA ALBRIGHT FINDS HERSELF EN-CHANTED BY THE RUGGED EGYPTOLOGIST ADAM CASSEL, BEHIND WHOSE ICY BLUE EYES BURNS A FIRE HOTTER THAN THE DESERT SUN."

MRS. CZER-**WICKI!** ROWR!

I'VE... ✷AHEM!✷ ALWAYS BEEN INTERESTED IN ARCHAE-OLOGY.

Peirce

74

PRINCIPAL NICHOLS! WHAT ARE YOU DOING OUT HERE?

JUST GREETING STUDENTS, THAT'S ALL!

IT'S SUCH A BEAUTIFUL DAY, I SIMPLY **HAD** TO BE OUTSIDE, SAYING "GOOD MORNING"!

I'M THE LEADER OF THIS SCHOOL, AND IT'S MY RESPONSIBILITY TO MAKE YOU KIDS FEEL **WELCOME**!

PLUS, MY OFFICE IS BEING PAINTED.

MR. GALVIN, CAN WE HAVE CLASS OUTSIDE? IT COULD BE **VERY** EDUCATIONAL!

LET'S GET OUT IN THE FIELD LIKE REAL SCIENTISTS! WE'LL STUDY ECOSYSTEMS! WE'LL DO RESEARCH!

YOU HAVE A FRISBEE HIDDEN IN YOUR NOTEBOOK.

THAT'S FOR COLLECTING SOIL SAMPLES.

THERE'S A HACKY SACK IN YOUR POCKET.

Peirce

MS. CLARKE, CAN WE HAVE CLASS OUTSIDE?

OUT-SIDE?

MR. ROSA SAID YES. MRS. GODFREY AND MR. GALVIN SAID NO.

ARE YOU GOING TO ALLY YOUR-SELF WITH ROSA, OR WITH GODFREY AND GALVIN?

WELL PLAYED.

I UNDER-STAND FACULTY DYNAMICS.

MR. STAPLES, IT'S SUCH A NICE DAY THAT WE'VE BEEN ASKING TEACHERS TO LET US HAVE CLASS OUTSIDE.

TWO TEACHERS HAVE SAID **YES**, TWO HAVE SAID **NO**. WE HAVE A **TIE**, AND ONLY **YOU** CAN BREAK IT!

THE CLOCK IS TICKING, MR. STAPLES.

IT'S HERO TIME.

SCORE! I HAPPEN TO KNOW THE MAN PLAYED DIVISION 3 BASKETBALL!

AHH, **SUMMER**!

NO SCHOOL TO THINK ABOUT! NO TEACHERS TO BOSS US AROUND! WE'RE **FREE**!

WE CAN DO ANYTHING WE WANT! THE POSSIBILITIES ARE ENDLESS! IT'S A BIG WORLD OUT THERE!

! MR. GALVIN!

YOU'RE JAYWALKING, BOYS. USE THE CROSS-WALK.

FIND SOMEWHERE ELSE TO PLAY FRISBEE, BOYS. YOU MIGHT HIT SOMEONE.

PRINCIPAL NICHOLS!

HOW'S THAT OFF-SEASON CONDITIONING PROGRAM GOING, LADIES?

COACH JOHN!

IF YOU WANT TO HAVE A **PRAYER** OF COMPLETING THE SUMMER READING LIST, I SUGGEST YOU HEAD FOR THE LIBRARY.

IT MIGHT BE A BIG WORLD, BUT IT'S A SMALL, SMALL TOWN.

I CAN'T WAIT TO GO OFF TO COLLEGE.

AWAKE ALREADY? DURING SUMMER VACATION?

YUP. I'M "SCHOOL-LAGGED."

MY BODY'S STILL ON A SCHOOL SCHEDULE, SO I WOKE UP AT 6:45, JUST LIKE A REGULAR SCHOOL DAY!

...BUT THERE **IS** NO SCHOOL, SO I'M GOING BACK TO BED! HAVE FUN AT WORK, DAD!

AND CAN YOU NOT SING IN THE SHOWER? THAT GIVES ME NIGHT-MARES.

Peirce

FRANCIS?... DUDE, HOW COME YOU'RE NOT AT THE BEACH? IT'S AWESOME! THE WATER IS **PERFECT!**

WHAT?... WELL, TELL YOUR MOM YOU'LL DO IT **LATER!** YOU CAN'T WASTE A PRIMO BEACH DAY LIKE THIS!

YEAH, THE BODY-SURFING IS **INCREDIBLE!** I'VE NEVER SEEN THE WAVES SO...

HELLO?

Peirce

WHAT'S WITH THE STICK?

JUST MAKING A POINT, TEDDY.

I KEEP TELLING COACH THAT NOTHING EVER HAPPENS OUT HERE IN RIGHT FIELD!

TO PROVE MY POINT, I'M MARKING THIS SPOT!

...AND I'LL BET I WON'T HAVE TO MOVE FROM THIS SPOT FOR THE WHOLE GAME!

CRACK!

WELL! LOOKS LIKE I **WILL** HAVE TO MOVE!

OOP! IT'S NOT CARRYING LIKE I THOUGHT IT WOULD!

ARRGH! NOW THE **WIND'S** TAKING IT!

THE SUN'S IN MY EYES! WHERE **IS** IT?

THERE IT IS!

NAB!

HERE COMES THE GIRL WITH THE SNACK CART! CAN WE GET A COUPLE SODAS, DAD?

OKAY. JUST LET ME HIT THIS SHOT.

WAK!

CLONG!

GOOD THING SHE WAS WEARING THAT BIKE HELMET.

I REALLY WASN'T THIRSTY ANYWAY.

Peirce

I LOVE GOLF, BUT I'VE NEVER REALLY PLAYED A ROUND THAT **MEANS** ANYTHING!

I'D LOVE TO KNOW WHAT IT WOULD FEEL LIKE TO BE A PRO! TO PLAY FOR **HIGH STAKES!**

I'D LOVE TO FIND OUT HOW I'D REACT UNDER **PRESSURE!**

YOU WANT PRESSURE?

YOU'RE DOWN TO YOUR LAST BALL, AND WE'RE ONLY ON THE TWELFTH HOLE.

YIKES.

"POOR NATE'S ALMANAC"? WHAT'S THIS?

I'M FOLLOWING IN THE FOOT-STEPS OF BEN FRANKLIN, BOYS!

POOR NATE'S ALMANAC $2

BACK IN THE 1700S, OL' BEN PUBLISHED "POOR RICHARD'S ALMANACK"!

IT WAS FILLED WITH ALL SORTS OF WISE SAY-INGS LIKE "THE EARLY BIRD GETS THE WORM" AND "A PENNY SAVED IS A PENNY EARNED"!

"POOR NATE'S ALMANAC" IS THE SAME THING, ONLY **BETTER**! YOU WON'T BELIEVE ALL THE WIS-DOM IN HERE!

POOR NATE'S

AND THESE ARE MY LAST TWO COPIES! A BARGAIN AT TWO BUCKS EACH!

OKAY, I'LL TAKE ONE.

ME TOO!

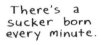

HEY! THIS THING'S **BLANK**!

WAIT, THERE'S SOMETHING WRITTEN ON THE LAST PAGE.

FLIP FLIP FLIP

There's a sucker born every minute.

THERE! THAT'S DONE!

WHAT'S DONE?

BOOP!

I JUST REGISTERED FOR MY FIRST ROAD RACE! A 10K!

COOL. CONGRATU- LATIONS, DAD.

☆CHUCKLE!☆... WELL, DON'T CONGRATULATE ME **NOW!** CONGRAT- ULATE ME WHEN I **FINISH** THE **RACE!**

WHAT IF YOU DON'T FINISH?

WHAT A CHEERY THOUGHT.

EXACTLY. ON RACE DAY I DON'T WANT TO BE, LIKE: "DAD! NICE **HEART ATTACK!**"

I DON'T WANT TO RAIN ON YOUR PARADE, DAD, BUT DO YOU REALLY THINK YOU CAN RUN A 10K?

WHY NOT?

IT'S OVER SIX MILES!

SO? LOOK, I ALREADY DO A DAILY LAP AROUND THE BLOCK!

TO TRAIN FOR THE RACE, ALL I NEED TO DO IS INCREASE THAT BY A LAP OR TWO!

...OR TWENTY-FOUR.

TWENTY-FOUR?

AND SPEAKING OF TRAINING... MIGHT BE A GOOD IDEA TO LOSE THE DOUGHNUT.

Peirce

DAD, IF YOU'RE GONNA RUN A 10K, YOU SHOULD LET ME BE YOUR TRAINER.

WHY'S THAT?

BECAUSE I KNOW WHAT I'M DOING! REMEMBER, I HAD TO RUN A 5-MILER TO GET MY PHYSICAL FITNESS MERIT BADGE!

THERE'S STUFF YOU NEED TO KNOW, DAD! THERE ARE "DO'S" AND "DON'TS" IN THE WORLD OF RUNNING!

THE SOCKS, FOR INSTANCE, ARE A "DON'T."

THEY ARE?

GOING FOR A TRAINING RUN, DAD? YOU NEED TO STRETCH FIRST.

BUT I STRETCHED ALREADY!

ALL YOU DID WAS LEAN AGAINST A WALL FOR FIVE SECONDS! BEND OVER AND TOUCH YOUR TOES FOR A TEN-COUNT!

OKAY.

RRIIP!

WAS THAT MY HAMSTRING?

JUST A WARDROBE MALFUNCTION, DAD. GO CHANGE YOUR SHORTS.

Peirce

OKAY, LADS, START LOOKING FOR STUFF WE CAN BUY CHEAP, THEN RESELL FOR A HUGE PROFIT!

YARD SALE

OH **HO!** A MAGIC EIGHT BALL!

A MAGIC EIGHT BALL? HOW IS **THAT** GONNA MAKE US A PROFIT?

MAGIC EIGHT BALL!... WILL FRANCIS, TEDDY AND I BUY SOMETHING AT THIS YARD SALE THAT'S WORTH **WAY** MORE THAN WE PAY FOR IT?

SHUCKA SHUCKA SHUCKA

"IT IS CERTAIN." **YES!**

I'M SO GLAD WE'RE APPROACHING THIS SCIENTIFICALLY.

GUYS, HELP ME PEEK BEHIND THE BACK OF THIS PAINTING!

WHAT FOR?

HAVEN'T YOU HEARD ABOUT THAT GUY WHO BOUGHT AN OLD PAINTING AT A YARD SALE?

LATER, WHEN HE TOOK OFF THE BACK-ING, HE FOUND A COPY OF THE **DECLARATION OF INDEPENDENCE!**

DUDE, THIS IS A VELVET SILKSCREEN OF DOGS PLAYING POKER.

EXACTLY! WHERE BETTER TO HIDE VALUABLES? BEHIND A **CLASSIC!**

MISTER, THIS YARD SALE ISN'T EXACTLY A TREASURE TROVE.

THERE'S NOTHING HERE I COULD TAKE TO "ANTIQUES ROADSHOW" AND FIND OUT IT'S WORTH A LOT OF MONEY! THERE'S NOTHING HERE OF **VALUE**!

IT'S ALMOST LIKE... YOU'RE JUST TRYING TO **SELL** STUFF YOU HAVE NO **USE** FOR ANYMORE!

NO OFFENSE.

NONE TAKEN. YOU GONNA BUY THAT?

THREE MORE, AND YOU'LL BREAK YOUR ALL-TIME RECORD!

NO PROBLEM!

SWISH!

TWO MORE! THAT'S PRESSURE SHOOTING!

"PRESSURE"? WHAT IS THIS "PRESSURE" YOU SPEAK OF?

SWISH!

I DON'T EVEN KNOW THE **MEANING** OF PRESSURE!

HELLO, BOYS.

MRS. GODFREY!

ULP!

I'M ON MY WAY OVER TO A READING AT THAT NEW BOOKSTORE!

HM.

UH HUH

OH, BUT I DIDN'T MEAN TO INTERRUPT YOU! KEEP SHOOTING, NATE!

UH... OKAY.

CLANG!

TSK! SO CLOSE!

NOW DO YOU KNOW THE MEANING OF PRESSURE?

OH, HOW I HATE HER.

CHESTER SEEMED SLUGGISH WARMING UP. HIS FASTBALL WAS SLOWER THAN USUAL.

I'LL FIX THAT.

CHESTER PITCHES BEST WHEN HE PITCHES **ANGRY!** SO ALL WE HAVE TO DO IS MAKE HIM **MAD!**

HOW DO WE...

YO, CHESTER! FRANCIS JUST CALLED YOU "SLOW"!

WHAT?!

THERE YOU GO! PROBLEM SOLVED!

Peirce

ATTABOY, CHESTER! NICE PITCHING!

IT'S GOOD THAT YOU CAUGHT THAT FLY BALL.

IF YOU HADN'T CAUGHT THAT FLY BALL, YOU WOULD HAVE MADE ME MAD.

IF YOU MISS ANY FLY BALLS DURING THE REST OF THE GAME, YOU'RE GOING TO MAKE ME MAD.

FOR THE FIRST TIME IN MY LIFE, I'M PRAYING FOR A RAIN OUT.

FRANCIS! DO YOU BELIEVE IN OMENS?

I GUESS SO.

WELL, IF I MAKE THIS SHOT, IT'S AN OMEN THAT I'M GOING TO BE RICH!

IF I MAKE IT WITHOUT HITTING THE BACKBOARD, IT MEANS I'M GOING TO BE FAMOUS!

...AND IF I MAKE IT WITHOUT HITTING THE BACKBOARD OR THE RIM, IT MEANS I'M GOING TO MARRY A SUPER-MODEL!

FLing!

CLANG!

CRASH!

MYOWR!

screeee... THUMP!

WHAT IF YOU MISS, AND THEN THE BALL BREAKS A WINDOW, HITS A CAT, ROLLS INTO THE STREET, AND GETS RUN OVER BY A DUMP TRUCK?

THEN IT'S A PRACTICE SHOT.

LOOK AT THAT TECHNIQUE! RUSTY SIENNA IS THE GREATEST PAINTER IN THE WORLD TODAY!

THEN WHAT'S HE DOING HOSTING A CHEESY TV SHOW? WHY ISN'T HE IN A MUSEUM OR SOMETHING?

LOOK, TEDDY, DON'T ASK ME TO EXPLAIN THE ABSURDITIES OF THE ART WORLD!

ALL I KNOW IS: WHEN RUSTY PAINTS A LAKE, IT LOOKS LIKE A LAKE! WHEN HE PAINTS A TREE, IT LOOKS LIKE A TREE! WHEN HE PAINTS AN ALP, IT LOOKS LIKE AN ALP!

"AN ALP"?

YOU CAN TELL IT'S AN ALP BECAUSE OF THE SHEPHERD GIRL IN THE CORNER.

WHAT'S UP?

I JUST GOOGLED RUSTY SIENNA! I'M THINKING OF SENDING HIM A FAN LETTER!

LET'S SEE..."RUSTY SIENNA, AMERICA'S FAVORITE TELEVISION ARTIST... BLAH BLAH BLAH... BORN APRIL 28TH, 1940.".

"DIED MAY 7TH, 1996."

WHAT?!

YOU KNOW, I **THOUGHT** HE LOOKED KIND OF PALE.

Peirce

I CAN'T **BELIEVE** THIS NEWS ABOUT RUSTY SIENNA! I'M IN **SHOCK**!

IT SAYS HERE HE DIED WHILE TAPING HIS TV SHOW, "OIL PAINTING WITH RUSTY," BACK IN 1996.

SO THE MAN I'VE IDOLIZED FOR MY WHOLE LIFE HAS BEEN SECRETLY **DEAD** THE ENTIRE TIME?

"SECRETLY DEAD"?

ACTUALLY, LET'S NOT THINK OF HIM AS "DEAD." LET'S THINK OF HIM AS "TIMELESS."

DAD, LET ME GIVE IT TO YOU STRAIGHT: I'M NOT SURE YOU'RE READY TO RUN A 10K.

OH, COME ON, NATE!

YOU ACT AS IF I'M TOTALLY INEXPERIENCED! I'LL HAVE YOU KNOW THAT I WAS A MEMBER OF MY HIGH SCHOOL TRACK TEAM!

YEAH, I KNEW THAT.

YOU DID?

I'VE SEEN YOUR YEARBOOK.

YOU HAVE?

HE WAS THE EQUIPMENT MANAGER.

BUSTED.

ARRGH!

WHAT'S UP, DAD?

I'VE BEEN TRYING TO FIGURE OUT THIS BRAIN TEASER FOR AN **HOUR**!

MAY I?

BE MY GUEST. IT'S **IMPOSSIBLE**!

MM.... MMM HMM...

GOT IT. THE SISTERS WERE BORN IN THIS ORDER: ELEANOR, EILEEN, ELIZABETH, EMILY AND EVELYN.

THAT WAS THE EASIEST BRAIN TEASER I'VE EVER SEEN.

THE PROBLEM WITH TEASING IS THAT IT OFTEN LEADS TO OUTRIGHT HUMILIATION.

THE RACE STARTS IN FIVE MINUTES!... I'M GETTING A LITTLE NERVOUS.

DAD, **DAD!** RE**LAX!**

REMEMBER: IT'LL ONLY LAST AN HOUR, AND THEN IT'LL BE OVER!

ACTUALLY, YOU'RE PRETTY SLOW... SO MAYBE IT'LL LAST AN HOUR AND A HALF.

YOU KNOW WHAT? TO BE SAFE, LET'S SAY TWO HOURS.

THANKS FOR YOUR SUPPORT.

WANT TO KNOW, ONCE AND FOR ALL, WHY CATS ARE BETTER THAN DOGS?

NOT REALLY.

THEY'RE MORE **AGILE!** COMPARED TO CATS, DOGS ARE SLOW AND CLUMSY!

HERE'S AN EXAMPLE: IF YOU DROPPED A CAT UPSIDE DOWN FROM A SECOND-FLOOR WINDOW, WHAT WOULD HAPPEN?

IT WOULD LAND ON ITS **FEET!**

NOW!... WHAT WOULD HAPPEN IF YOU DROPPED A **DOG** UPSIDE DOWN FROM THAT VERY SAME SECOND-FLOOR WINDOW?

IT WOULD LAND ON THE CAT.

HIGH FIVE!

THAT'S WHY YOU DROP THE CAT FIRST!

WHERE **IS** IT? I REMEMBER BURYING MY TIME CAPSULE **RIGHT HERE**!

MAYBE YOUR MEMORY IS WRONG.

MY MEMORY IS **PERFECT!** I REMEMBER DIGGING FOR HOURS IN THE BLAZING SUN, AND IT WAS ALL DUSTY, AND I FOUND THIS LITTLE THING WITH INITIALS ON IT, AND...

DUDE, THAT WAS "HOLES." WE WATCHED IT AT MY HOUSE LAST WEEK.

WELL, THAT WOULD EXPLAIN THE PRESENCE OF JON VOIGHT.

HE'S EASILY CONFUSED.

WAIT 'TIL I FIND MY TIME CAPSULE! MY BLUE RIBBON FROM THE PIE-EATING CONTEST IS IN THERE... THERE'S A TICKET STUB FROM A SOX-ORIOLES GAME...

THERE'S A HAIKU I WROTE IN SECOND GRADE... A PICTURE OF ME AND MY UNCLE DAVE...

IF YOU RE-MEMBER EVERYTHING THAT'S IN THERE, WHAT'S THE POINT OF DIGGING IT UP?

SHUT UP.

JACKPOT! I KNEW IT WAS HERE! I FOUND MY TIME CAPSULE!

...AND... YES! THEY SURVIVED! THEY DIDN'T DECOMPOSE!

"CHEEZ DOODLES" CAN LAST FOR THREE YEARS BURIED IN A CIGAR BOX FOUR FEET UNDERGROUND!!

WANT ONE?

ONLY IF YOU ALSO BURIED SOME "PEPTO-BISMOL"!

☆CRUNCH☆... A LITTLE BIT GRITTY, BUT STILL "PUFF-A-LICIOUS."

The Monday known as Labor Day
Is cause for celebration;
A tribute to the efforts of
All those who've built this nation.

How is this day devoted to
The "Working Man" observed?
We leave our jobs behind and take
A rest most well-deserved.

I say to you: enjoy yourself!
And seize the day, my friend.
For when tomorrow rolls around...

...The grind begins again.

Public School 38

WELCOME BACK
STUDENTS

I CAN'T **BELIEVE** I'M LOCKER PARTNERS WITH AMANDA! HOW LUCKY CAN I **GET**?!

SHARING A LOCKER MEANS I GET TO SEE HER SEVERAL TIMES EVERY DAY! WE'LL HANG OUT...GET TO KNOW EACH OTHER...

KLIK!

FOOM!

HAVE YOU CONSIDERED THE DOWNSIDE?

WHAT DOWNSIDE?

RRRRINNNGG!!

TAKE YOUR SEATS, PEOPLE. NATE, SPIT OUT THAT GUM.

DON'T JUST SPIT IT INTO THE **CAN**, FOR GOODNESS SAKE!! WRAP IT IN SOME **PAPER** FIRST!

NOT THAT PAPER! THAT'S MY **ATTENDANCE SHEET!**

IT'S ALMOST AS IF SUMMER VACATION NEVER EVEN HAPPENED!

OH, HOW I HATE HER.

MS. CLARKE JUST TOLD ME SHE AND MRS. GODFREY ARE **BEST FRIENDS!**

OH, YEAH. THEY'RE REAL CLOSE.

I SAW THEM RIDING LAST WEEK AT THE STABLES WHERE I TAKE LESSONS.

WAIT, WAIT. MRS. GODFREY RODE A **HORSE?**

IS THE HORSE OKAY?

APPARENTLY IT'S A CRIMINAL OFFENSE TO SHOW CONCERN FOR ANIMAL WELFARE.

PRINCIPAL

SO! THE TASK AT HAND, AS I UNDERSTAND IT, IS TO WHIP YOU MARSHMALLOWS INTO **SHAPE**!

THAT'LL TAKE **WORK**, SOLDIERS! **LOTS** OF WORK! BUT JUST REMEMBER **THIS**:

"THAT WHICH DOES NOT **KILL** ME MAKES ME **STRONGER**"!!

SO HE'S ONLY GOING TO **ALMOST** KILL US?

GULP!

FIRST RULE: IF YOU'RE GOING TO TOSS YOUR COOKIES, DO IT ON THE **SIDELINES**!

Peirce

176

REMEMBER THAT BAND THAT PLAYED AT THE SPRING DANCE?

"THE DIS- TEMPERS"?

WHAT ABOUT THEM?

WELL, THEY WERE JUST A BUNCH OF HIGH SCHOOL KIDS, RIGHT? WHY COULDN'T **WE** DO THAT?

I COULD DO EVERYTHING THAT **THEIR** LEAD SINGER DID!

I TOTALLY AGREE!...

...ESPECIALLY THE PART WHERE HE SNEEZED DURING "STAIRWAY TO HEAVEN," THEN FELL OFF THE STAGE!

YEAH, THAT IS **SO** YOU!

"ENSLAVE THE MOLLUSK"? **THAT'S** THE NAME OF OUR BAND?

A GOOD NAME IS THE FIRST STEP TO STARDOM, TEDDY!

...AND THE **SECOND** STEP IS TO START PLAYING GIGS! THE MORE GIGS WE PLAY, THE MORE FAMOUS WE'LL GET!

GIGS?

GIGS!

JUST SAYING THE WORD "GIGS" MAKES ME FEEL LIKE A WORLD-CLASS CHEESE BALL.

CAN WE GO BACK TO THE PART WHERE YOU CALLED "ENSLAVE THE MOLLUSK" A GOOD NAME?

PRETTY COOL, EH GUYS? MY DAD SAID WE COULD USE THE GARAGE FOR BAND PRACTICE!

SOON THE NEIGHBORHOOD WILL BE FILLED WITH THE SOUNDS OF "ENSLAVE THE MOLLUSK" PLAYING HEAD-BANGING, EARTH-SHATTERING ROCK!

WHO BROUGHT SOME MUSIC?

I DID! TWO SONGS!

MY "HOT CROSS BUNS" IS PRETTY GOOD, BUT MY "BAA BAA BLACK SHEEP" NEEDS A LITTLE WORK.

THAT'S GOOD TO KNOW.

YOU'RE THE NICKNAME CZAR, RIGHT? I HAVE A NEW NICKNAME FOR MRS. GODFREY!

LET'S HEAR IT.

"CRUELLA"! 'CAUSE, YOU KNOW, SHE'S SO MEAN!

HM. NOPE. SORRY, GUY.

THAT'S TOO STRAIGHTFORWARD! A GOOD NICKNAME WORKS ON **MANY** LEVELS!

TAKE ONE OF MY FAVORITE NAMES FOR MRS. GODFREY: "DARK SIDE OF THE MOON"!

THE "DARK SIDE," OBVIOUSLY, REFERS TO MRS. GODFREY'S SOUL. SHE HAS TURNED TO THE DARK SIDE AND EMBRACED EVIL AS A WAY OF LIFE.

THE MOON, LIKE MRS. GODFREY, IS HUGE, INHOSPITABLE AND DEVOID OF BEAUTY.

AND FINALLY, THE MOON'S DARK SIDE IS EXTREMELY COLD — EXACTLY LIKE MRS. GODFREY, WHO HAS NO WARMTH OR KINDNESS.

KEEP TRYING, KID.

THE GREAT ONES MAKE IT LOOK SO EASY.

HOW COME **YOU** GET TO BE NICKNAME CZAR?

HM?

I'M CHALLENGING YOU, NATE! **I** CAN COME UP WITH BETTER NICK-NAMES THAN **YOU** CAN!

WE'LL HAVE A CONTEST!

EACH OF YOU HAS TO COME UP WITH A NICKNAME **ON THE SPOT** FOR THE FIRST TEACHER WHO WALKS BY!

TEDDY AND I WILL JUDGE!

AND REMEMBER: A GOOD NICKNAME WORKS ON **MANY** LEVELS!

GUYS! COACH JOHN!

UMM... LET'S SEE HERE...

"FAST BREAK."

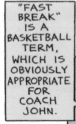

"FAST BREAK" IS A BASKETBALL TERM, WHICH IS OBVIOUSLY APPROPRIATE FOR COACH JOHN.

...BUT THE WORD "FAST" IS IRONIC, BECAUSE COACH JOHN IS SO SLOW.

ALSO, "FAST BREAK" IS A PLAY ON WORDS. WHEN YOU BREAK A FAST, YOU **EAT.** CLEARLY, COACH JOHN HAS BROKEN A FEW FASTS IN HIS DAY.

I KNOW WHEN I'M BEATEN.

LONG LIVE THE CZAR!

HELLO, "OLDIES 98.9"? WHAT'S UP WITH YOU GUYS? YOU USED TO PLAY STUFF FROM THE SIXTIES AND SEVENTIES!

NOW YOU'RE PLAYING **CYNDI LAUPER** SONGS! CYNDI LAUPER IS **NOT** AN **OLDIE**!

UH... NO, I HAVEN'T SEEN HER LATELY.

THEY'VE GOT A POINT THERE.

HI, "OLDIES 98.9"? CAN YOU PLAY "LITTLE BITTY PRETTY ONE" BY THURSTON HARRIS? WHAT?... WHY NOT?

YES, I **KNOW** YOU'VE CHANGED YOUR FORMAT, BUT... WHAT?... WELL, YOU'RE STILL CALLING YOURSELF AN OLDIES STATION! WHY CAN'T I REQUEST AN OLDIE?

WHAT DO YOU MEAN, "THAT'S **TOO** OLD"? LISTEN, YOU CAN'T... WHAT?... WHAT DOES IT MATTER HOW OLD **I** AM? LET ME TELL YOU SOMETHING, SONNY, I'M NOT... HELLO? **HELLO?**

I NEVER KNEW EXACTLY WHAT THE PHRASE "MIDLIFE CRISIS" MEANT UNTIL JUST NOW.

I'VE SWITCHED RADIO STATIONS! NO MORE OBSESSING OVER WHAT SONGS THEY SHOULD BE PLAYING ON "OLDIES 98.9"!

FROM NOW ON, I'M LISTENING TO "THE HAMMER 103.7"! THEY PLAY ONLY "CLASSIC ROCK"!

WHAT THE...? IS THIS REO SPEEDWAGON? THEY'RE PLAYING **REO SPEEDWAGON?!**

REO SPEED-WAGON IS NOT CLASSIC ROCK!!

I'LL BE OUT-SIDE.

GOOD NEWS, GUYS! MY DAD'S LETTING ME THINK UP A MIDDLE NAME FOR MYSELF!

I'M STILL MULLING IT OVER, BUT A CLEAR FRONT-RUNNER HAS EMERGED!

LET'S HEAR IT.

"MAXIMUS"!

VERY MODEST.

IS THAT A NAME OR A MALE ENHANCEMENT SUPPLEMENT?

GUYS, HELP ME PICK OUT A GOOD MIDDLE NAME!

I'VE NARROWED IT DOWN TO CAESAR, SOLOMON, ARTHUR, ALEXANDER...

...AUGUSTUS, ZEUS, CONSTANTINE, HENRY, CHARLEMAGNE, AND JUSTINIAN!

I'M DETECTING A THEME.

EVER HEARD THE PHRASE, "NAPOLEON COMPLEX"?

OOH, NAPOLEON! THAT'S A GOOD ONE!

I'VE DECIDED TO STOP LOOKING FOR A MIDDLE NAME.

"NATE WRIGHT" IS A SIMPLE NAME, BUT SOMETIMES LESS IS MORE! SOMETIMES SIMPLE IS **GOOD**!

A SIMPLE NAME FOR A SIMPLE PERSON?

ExACTLY!

EXACTLY.

DAD, HAVE YOU EVER THOUGHT ABOUT HOW THIS AFFECTS **ME?**

HOW WHAT AFFECTS YOU?

THE WHOLE HALLOWEEN THING! EVERYBODY KNOWS THAT **MY DAD** IS THE NIMROD WHO HANDS OUT **PRUNES** TO TRICK-OR-TREATERS!

DO YOU HAVE ANY IDEA HOW EMBARRASSING THAT IS FOR ME?

DID YOU JUST CALL ME A NIMROD?

FIRE UP THE **SHAME-CAM,** FOLKS! I'M READY FOR MY **CLOSE-UP!**

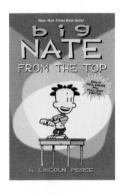
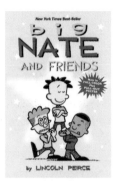

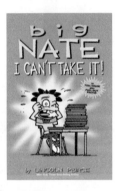

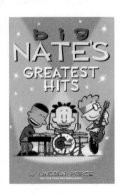